Business, Economics, Finance, Monetary

DAVID HAMMOND

TOM LESTER

JOE SCALES

DALE SEYMOUR PUBLICATIONS®

Managing Editor: Catherine Anderson
Production/Manufacturing Director: Janet Yearian
Production/Manufacturing Coordinator: Karen Mancinelli
Design Director: Phyllis Aycock
Design Manager: Jeff Kelly
Text and Cover Design: Nita Ybarra Design
Composition and Computer Graphics: Eileen Sullivan

ISBN 0-7690-0126-2
Printed in the United States of America
3 4 5 6 7 8 9 06 05 04 03

ACKNOWLEDGEMENTS

★

We would like to thank the *Sacramento Bee* for eighteen years of support by having a Plexer appear daily on the comic page. We appreciate the thousands of teachers and students who have made Plexers a part of their school programs, both as an academic tool and as a mind-expanding recreational pastime. We have published nearly 6,000 different Plexers. The encouragement to produce topical books came from subject matter teachers who through the years have asked, "Don't you have subject-centered Plexers that I can use with my students?" You are holding the result. We trust that we have met your expectations. To all of you Plexer fans, a big thank you!

David Hammond

Tom Lester

Joe Scales

INTRODUCTION

★

PLEXER is derived from the word perplex which means; "to confuse or puzzle; bewilder, to make confusedly intricate." It is the the prime objective of Plexer books to encourage students to think logically and to expand the ways in which they view the world and solve problems.

Divergent thinking is at the heart of Plexers. It gives students another communication code. Plexers allow them to try different solutions without risk, since there are no grades when solving Plexers. The possibility of developing an original piece of work is very high with Plexers. To invent something no one has ever seen before is very exciting.

Plexers are always associated with a Plexer box. The words and symbols placed in and around it stand for expressions, idioms, people, events, objects, and, in general, things that students are familiar with to some extent. The Plexer box gives license to use spelling and grammatical errors that are not acceptable in students' daily work. This has an appeal that motivates even the most precise student.

It is important that those who know the solution to a Plexer do not spoil the enjoyment of others discovering it on their own. An essential stage of problem solving, the "incubation stage," is rare in America's classrooms. Teachers are so used to "telling" and having closure that they forget students need to develop internal processes that advance data into a sequenced understanding. It is important to instruct for process as well as knowledge.

Using Arithmetic Plexers in the Classroom.

- Mathematics has many symbols that also can mean other things. Pi , for example, sounds like pie. The symbol for Pi (π) when used in Plexers can be a different way of saying a common dessert such as "apple π." Teachers can have students develop Plexers from symbols such as π.

- Teachers may post a group of 2 or 3 Plexers on the bulletin board. At a convenient time of the day, ask students if they have a conjecture of what any of the Plexers mean. Difficult Plexers may stay on the board for a couple of days or longer. Invite students who have solved one or more of the Plexers to provide a new hint each day for those who have not.

- Include Plexers on worksheets, tests or quizzes as a last question or as a problem solving item. Some Plexers may have several solutions. Make a list of them and discuss the merits of each solution. There are no right and wrong answers. If the solution meets the Plexer's symbolism, it is acceptable.

- Provide a page of Plexers to students. Have them work individually, in pairs, or in groups to solve the Plexers. Have students explain how they solved each Plexer. Use the discussion to refine problem solving strategies.

- Have students identify types of Plexers, giving samples of each type. For example, "location" could be one of the types. Under "location" students would include examples of the location of the Plexers in relation to the Plexer box: on the sides, down low, up high, in or out, in the middle, or even in corners. Students soon realize that location often becomes part of the solution for many of the Plexers.

- Use Plexers at the end of a class to keep minds occupied and prevent "downtime." Plexers also make good warm-up activities when returning to school after a long holiday.

- Have students choose their favorite Plexers and tell why they are favorites. This provides the students an opportunity to express their personal preferences for a variety of thought processes. Students will often choose one they created as their favorite, reinforcing the importance of being creative. Plexer creation is another form of creativity and is just as beneficial as creative art, music and writing.

- As a general rule, the difficulty level of the Plexers increases from the beginning to the end of a page.

- Most importantly, Plexers are for fun! It is the authors' fondest wish that everyone enjoy the challenge of Plexers.

1

$ BURN
BURN

2

ENDEND

3

COST

4

COMPUTER

5

7

CHANGE

6

SURCARANCE

7

MAKING $

H

FIST

8

$\sqrt{\text{PROBLEM}}$

9

MOSTOLENEY

10

YAP

11

BUY

12

N
O
PAYOT

13

8T

ARITHMETIC
PLEXERS®

14

RENT
DUE

15

P P
HEAVEN
N N
N N
Y Y

16

T T

17

¢ 4A $

18

CHARGING CUSTOMERS

19

b♫nk

20

<u>COMPUTER</u>

21

U ~~GET~~
+ THING
4 0

22

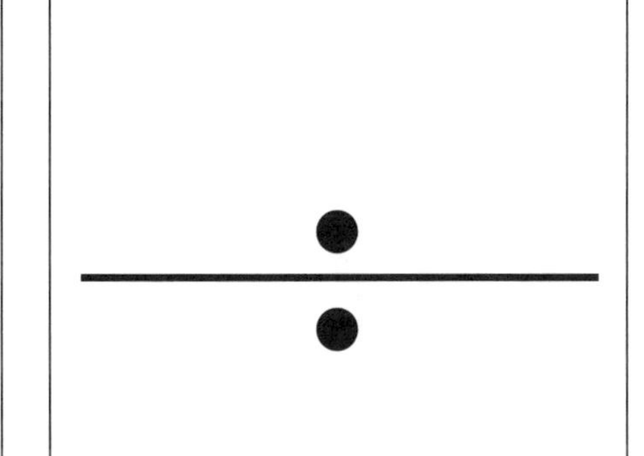

23

DoftOR

24

$ a ROO

25

26

RI
MONEY
LG
L

27

28

29

DIFFE RENCE

30

DEBIT RATIO

31

1%2%3%

32

CO – ME
TAX

33

ON
TI
UC
OD
PR

34

★★★★RULE

35

SELLER

36

BET

MY

$

37

M
A
K
E
$

38

FUND

39

BB=2

40

41

42

"TIENT"

43

DIOSION

44

TAX TAX TAX

45

HSAC
ER

46

EZ $

47

CHART

ARITHMETIC
PLEXERS®

48

$ & ¢

49

P
JONE
JONE
K

50

VE$TOT

51

E
M C
A I
R
P K
E
T

52

FILING
FILING

53

AWE +

54

++

55

MACHINE
+ MACHINE

ARITHMETIC
PLEXERS®

56

A1, A2, A3,
A4, A5, ...

57

P A R

58

¢ —

59

OAGEOT

60

XAT
XAT

61

62

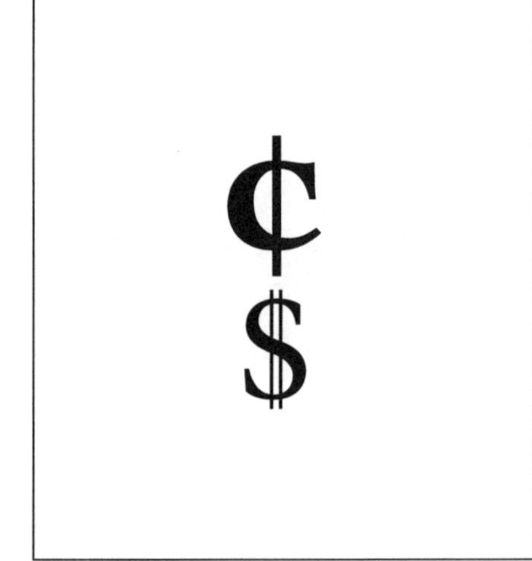

63

$$\begin{array}{r} X \\ + X \\ \hline \end{array}$$

64

65

$ BAIL

66

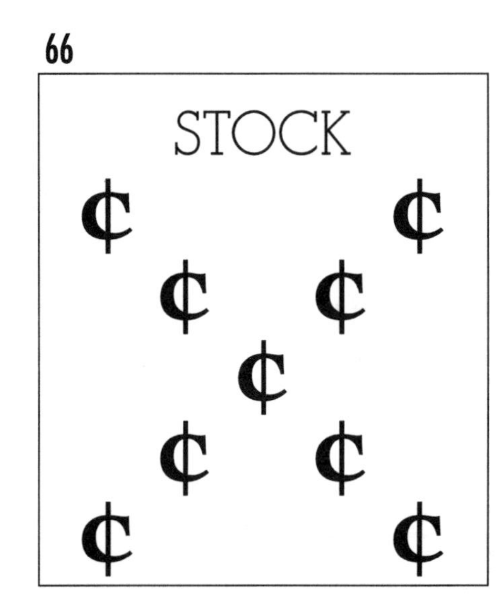

67

LIVE
(time)

68

PAYOT
PENALTY

69

70

T
R
I
ECONOMICS
K
L
E

71

BANK
IT

72

HAND HAND
HAND HAND
HAND WORK HAND
HAND HAND

73

T T T T

74

75

PAYPAYPAYPAY

76

PRICE (top half only)

77

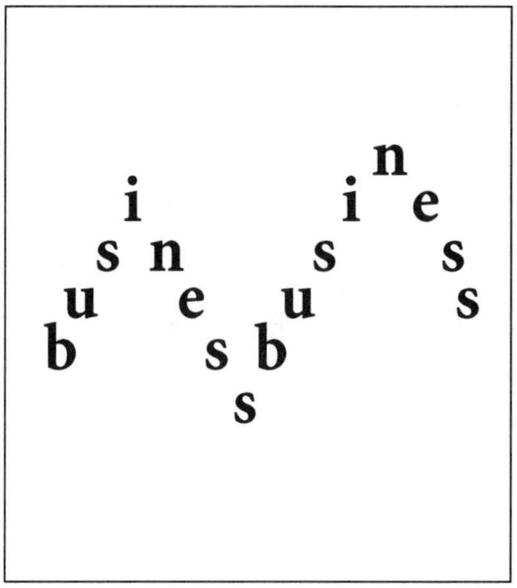

b u s i n e s s b u s i n e s s

78

HE HE
DEDAEHBT

79

— —

ARITHMETIC ★ PLEXERS®

80

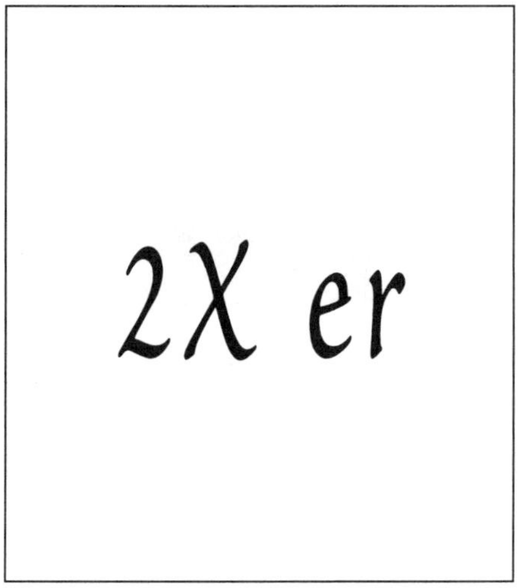

2X er

81

A✔✔OUNT

82

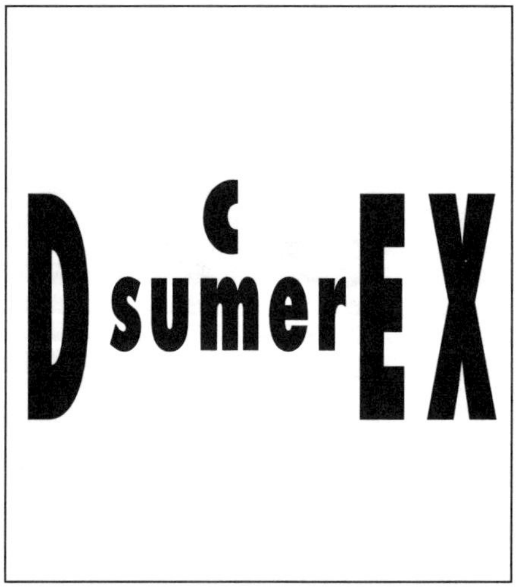

D c sumer EX

83

NATIONAL
NATIONAL Inc.
NATIONAL

84

lonely

85

+ DISHNL

86

87

ARITHMETIC ★ PLEXERS®

88

89

INDEMNITY
INDEMNITY

90

E
D
A UR SKILLS
R
G

91

RETIEF

92

NERS

93

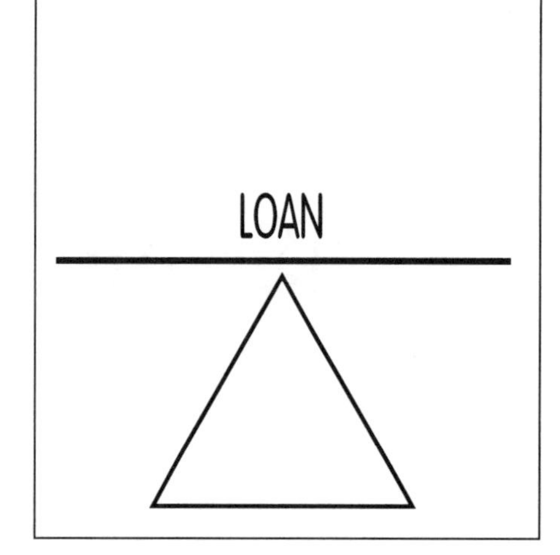

94

X10SIVE

95

PRIORITY

96

¢ yy

97

♂ UFACTURE

98

S
I
Z
I
N
G

99

GLASS

100

OG
1'S
WORD

101

GOOUT

102

¢—

103

GAIN
GAIN

104

HELDTAX

105

♂
NIGHT

106

¢
YY
ƒ
Lb
FOOLISH

107

Ci2i

108

? THAT
THAT

109
DAYSALLWORK
110
STOCK STOCK STOCK STOCK STOCK STOCK STOCK STOCK STOCK STOCK STOCK STOCK STOCK STOCK STOCK STOCK STOCK
111
$
2
112
GONE
GONE C
GONE CLUSION
GONE
113
LOG
114
D+EX
115
VANTAGE
+ VANTAGE
116
DRIVE
WINDOW
117
TEMPORARILY
JOBOJOB

118

SALES O SHIP

119

120

S

BASICS

121

L

I

E

JOB

122

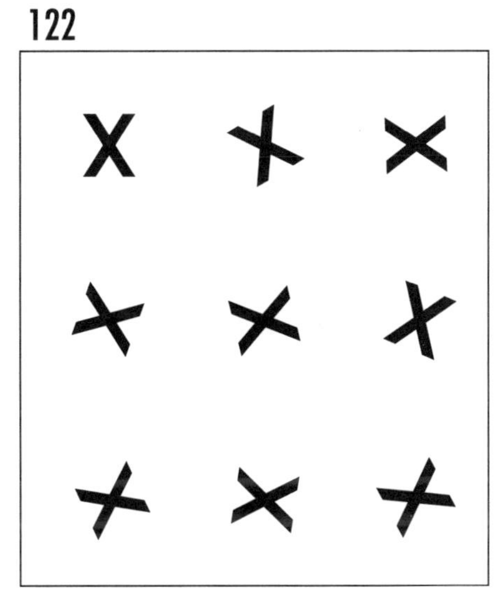

123

124

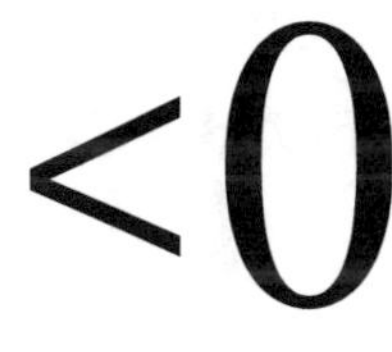

125

πR8

126

COTAXME

127

F ND
FU D
UND

128

post

129

10ANT

130

♂ DATORY

131

ESTIMATE
$

132

& reach
touch
+ 1

133

GO
GO
RAGS
↓
RICH
RICH

134

FUR

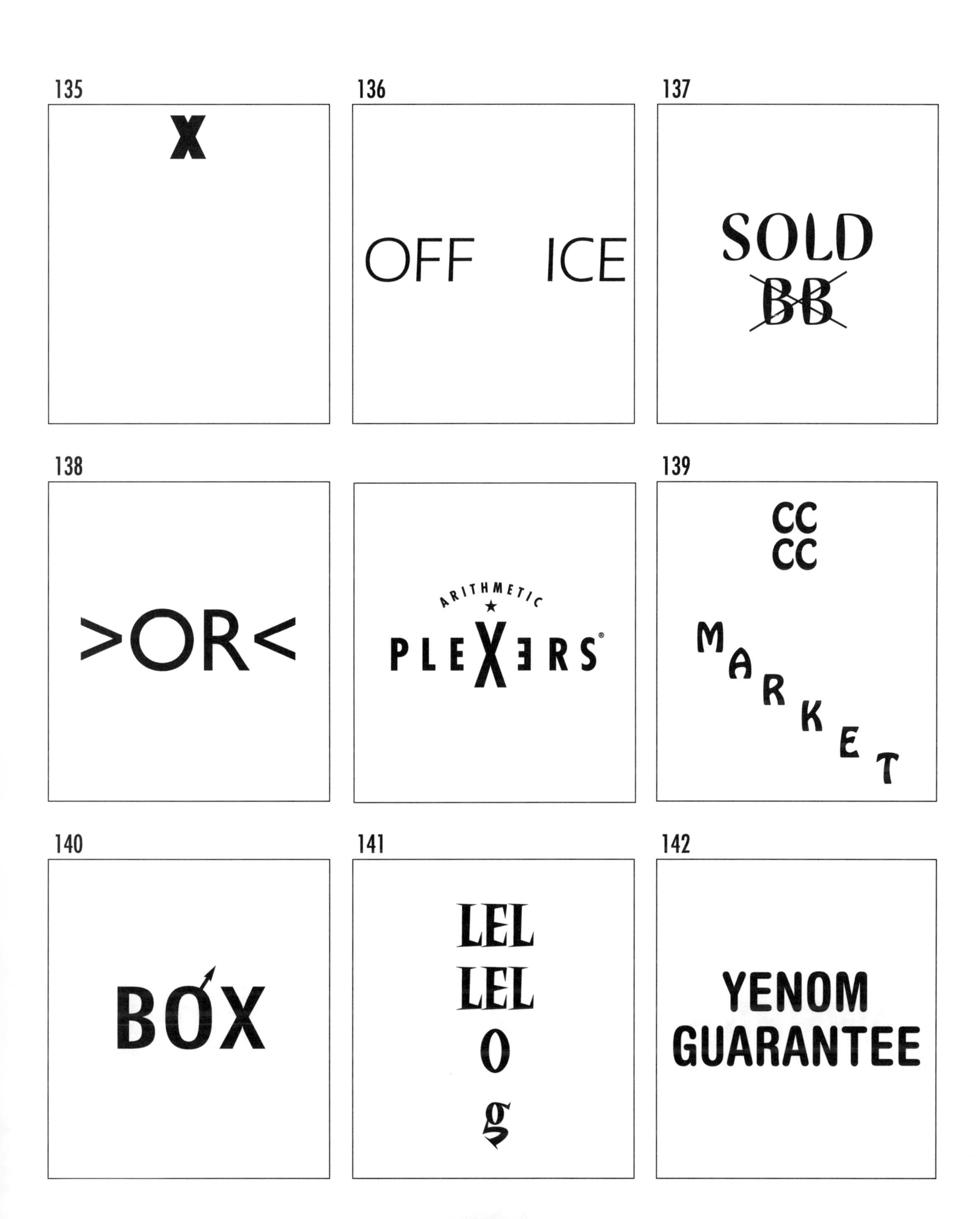
135
X
136
OFF ICE
137
SOLD
BB
138
>OR<
ARITHMETIC
PLEXƎRS
139
CC
CC
MARKET
140
BOX
141
LEL
LEL
O
g
142
YENOM
GUARANTEE

143
INCOME
144
ICE
145
B
DUTY
146
BID
147
148
HAD
DAY DAY
149
AWHBILE
150
151
COME

152

$\frac{1}{2}$

153

C4AR
CA4R

154

F E E T
T F
E E
E E
F E E T

155

SUB

156

+ O − ¢

157

2,3
5,7
. . .
R8

158

STAY

R
BUSINESS
MUST

159

$STEAK^3$

160

NE+IED

161

BID
144LY

162

BUSINES

163

~~MY~~
ACCOUNT

164

OHEHE ¢

ARITHMETIC
★
PLEXERS®

165

MBA
S
C
H
O
O
L

166

I'M
TAKING
LUNCH
DAY
DAY

167

KROW
KROW

168

+Rii

169

HO U SE

170

PAID

RU

171

SALE

K
R
A
M

172

B D
R N
A
R N
B D

ARITHMETIC

★

PLEXƎRS®

173

TILPSPLIT

174

ANNUAL

ND

175

WR
WOR
WORK
WORK
WORK
ORK
RK

176

B A N K

177

SALES

178

COST
RUN

179

CHABRGE

180

A ER

181

182

STUDY
ABLE

183

LY
―
4

PAYOT

184

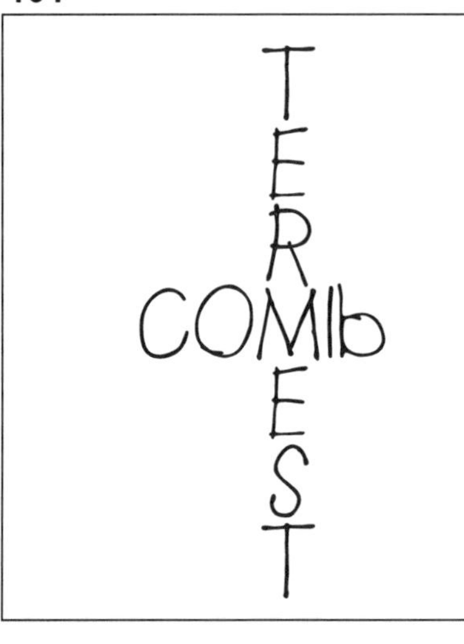

185

C
+VANCE
L
L

186

COPY

187

PRICE

188

PONENT
PONENT

189

S
T
I
F
ROOF
R
P

ARITHMETIC PLEXERS®

190

MAKE $
PAPER

191

192

CLOSE

193

– $ FLOW

194

HEAD

195

OG

2

1^2

196

SHOT

197

•
•
•
C
A
L
L
•
•
•

•
•
•
C
A
L
L
•
•
•

ARITHMETIC ★ PLEXERS®

198

241 STOCK

199

YES ♂

200

DEDUCTIONS
ESTIMATE

201

ENUT
ENUT
ENUT
ENUT

202

COUPON
COUPON

203

TIME
WORKER

204

DIS 1,2,3, ...

205

PA10T

ARITHMETIC
PLEXERS®

206

E
D
CHIEF
T
O
R

207

SYSTEM
RIDE

208

4
WHAT
U
DO
PAID

209

SIR +

210

YIELD

BOND
BOND

211

SHEET

212

E¢ONOMY

213

F A S H I
F A S O
H N
I
O
N

ARITHMETIC
PLEXERS®

214

OCCUPANCY
OCCUPANCY

215

FLIGHT
BOOKED

216

HAND

217

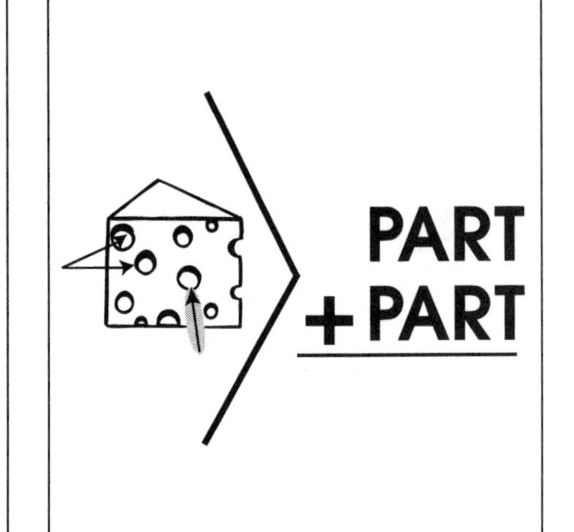

218

T
E
K
R
A
M

219

$LENDER

220

OFFEBRING

221

$ A ✔

ARITHMETIC
★
PLEXERS®

222

RETURN

INVESTMENT

223

BUSINESS
PLAN

R
E
A
D

224

PUT IT
RENRUB

225

CO1'sME
SPEND

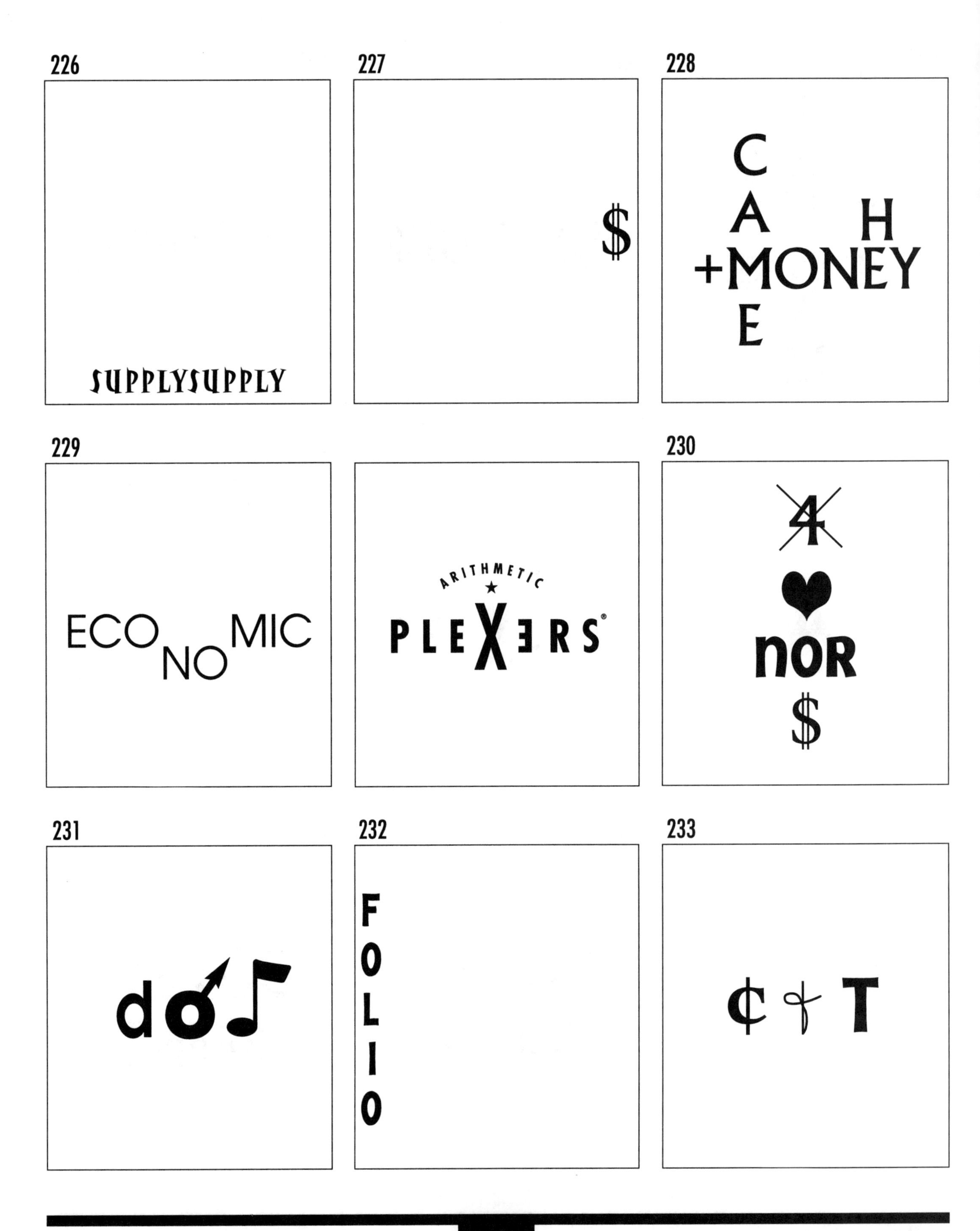
226
SUPPLYSUPPLY
227
$
228
C
A
H
+MONEY
E
229
ECO
NO
MIC
ARITHMETIC
PLEXERS
230
4
nor
$
231
do
232
F
O
L
I
O
233
¢
T

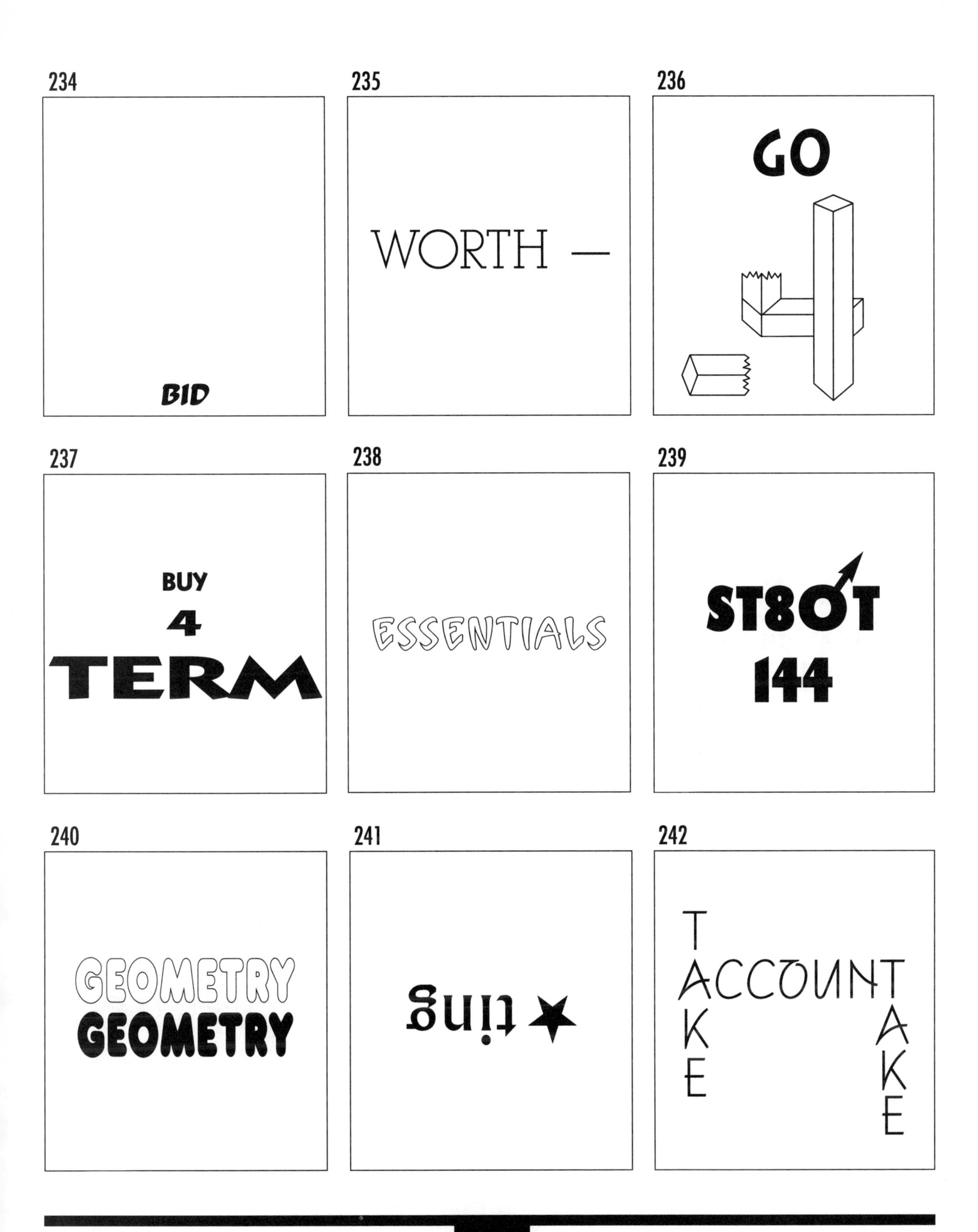
234
BID
235
WORTH —
236
GO
237
BUY
4
TERM
238
ESSENTIALS
239
ST8OT
144
240
GEOMETRY
GEOMETRY
241
ting ★
242
T
ACCOUNT
K
E
A
K
E

243

PER¢AGE

244

CLUTAXDED

245

SAVE
+
$

246

SALARY

247

PAY ✓✓

248

249

T
N
O
R
F

$

250

AN

251

VESTYYOT

252

SEND
ERRAND

253

SALE
SALE
SALE
SALE
OWNER

254

$
+
CARRY

255

TAKE
TASK

256

DAY DAY

257

+1

258

✓

259

• UL8

260

DRAWAL
ATM
DRAWAL

261

— GRAPH

262

¢

263

"WORM

264

PENSION ꓤOꓶꓶ

ARITHMETIC PLEXERS®

265

SW♥ET DEAL

266

TWO

267

BOLA
BOLA

268

BUSINESS

♂UAL

ANSWERS

★

page 1

1. money to burn
2. making ends meet
3 cost reduction
4 computer crashed
5. spare change
6. car insurance
7. making money hand over fist
8. root of the problem
9. stolen money

page 2

10. back pay
11. buy out
12. no down payment
13. eighty
14. the rent is overdue
15. pennies from heaven
16. parity
17. change for a dollar

page 3

18. overcharging customers
19. bank note
20. online computer; comuter online
21. you can't get something for nothing
22. long division
23. foot in the door
24. buckaroo
25. credit balance
26. rolling in money

page 4

27. even split
28. she's short on cash
29. split the difference
30. high debit ratio
31. 3 percent inflation
32. negative income tax
33. step up production
34. general rule

page 5

35. top seller
36. bet my bottom dollar
37. make money on the side
38. growth fund
39. to be equal to
40. a balanced checkbook
41. in less than no time
42. quotient
43. dimension

page 6

44. raising taxes
45 cash back offer
46 easy money
47. flipchart
48. dollars and cents
49. keep up with the Jones's
50. cash investment
51. rising price in a falling market

page 7

52. filing jointly
53. awesome
54. bargains
55. adding machines
56. accounting
57. parlay
58. senseless
59. management

page 8

60. back taxes
61. drum up business
62. pennies on the dollar
63. sometimes (sum times)

64. over the counter stock
65. monetary bailout
66. stock exchange
67. live on borrowed time

page 9

68. underpayment penalty
69. the check is in the mail
70. trickle down economics
71. don't bank on it
72. many hands make light work
73. a t-square
74. times change
75. payroll

page 10

76. half price
77. business ups and downs
78. he's overhead in debt
79. double negative
80. two timer
81. checking account
82. consumer index
83. multi-national corporation

page 11

84. It's lonely at the top
85. additional
86. the bottom line
87. white out
88. save big bucks
89. double indemnity
90. upgrade your skills
91. counterfeiter

page 12

92. partners
93. small loan balance
94. extensive
95. high priority
96. penny-wise
97. manufacture
98. downsizing
99. glass ceiling
100. go back on one's word

page 13

101. go without
102. left penniless
103. capital gains
104. tax withheld
105. overnight mail
106. penny wise and pound foolish
107. see eye to eye
108. that's beside the question

page 14

109. all in a day's work
110. stock pile
111. half dollar ($.50)
112. foregone conclusion
113. backlog
114. cross index
115. advantages
116. drive through window
117. temporarily between jobs

page 15

118. salesmanship
119. check point
120. back to basics
121. lie down on the job
122. changing times
123. the bottom fell out of the market
124. less than nothing
125. pirate

page 16

126. income tax
127. insufficient funds
128. postmarked
129. tenant
130. mandatory
131. estimate right on the money
132. "reach out and touch someone"
133. to go from rags to riches
134. furlong

page 17

135. high times
136. office space
137. not to be undersold
138. more or less
139. foresee a market downturn
140. mail box
141. parallelogram
142. money back guarantee

page 18

143. low income
144. dead letter office
145. be on duty
146. high bid
147. split up the money
148. had your break today?
149. be back in awhile
150. double check with her
151. net income

page 19

152. half right
153. foreign cars
154. square feet
155. subdivided
156. adolescent
157. prime rate
158. our business must stay on top
159. cubed steak
160. someone in need

page 20

161. grossly under bid
162. unfinished business
163. not on my account
164. he's innocent
165. the right business school
166. I'm taking a long lunch today
167. back to work
168. summarize

page 21

169. open house
170. are you underpaid?
171. wholesale mark-up
172. brand-X
173. two-way split
174. semiannual dividend
175. network
176. bankroll

page 22

177. sales slip
178. cost overrun
179. be in charge
180. note paper
181. turn it in under the deadline
182. an able understudy
183. quarterly payment
184. compound interest
185. call in advance

page 23

186. copyright
187. price reduction
188. exponents
189. profits going through the roof
190. make money on paper
191. cut a deal
192. close out
193. negative cash flow

page 24

194. low overhead
195. go back to square one
196. big shot
197. marginal calls
198. two for one stock split
199. yes man
200. over estimate deductions
201. reverse of fortune

page 25

202. double coupons
203. part time worker
204. discount
205. patent
206. editor-in-chief
207. system override
208. overpaid for what you do
209. surplus

page 26

210. high-yield bonds
211. spreadsheet
212. small change in the economy
213. fall fashions
214. double occupancy
215. overbooked flight
216. shorthand
217. the whole is greater than the sum of the parts

page 27

218. the market is up
219. money lender
220. be in the offering
221. cash a check
222. high return, low investment
223. business plan readout
224. put it on the back burner
225. overspend one's income

page 28

226. supplies are low
227. price is right
228. he came into some money
229. economic depression
230. not for love nor money
231. demand note
232. portfolio (left folio)
233. penny ante

page 29

234. low bid
235. worthless
236. go for broke
237. buy for the long term
238. bare essentials
239. gross understatement
240. plane and solid geometry
241. starting over
242. takes into account

page 30

243. percentage
244. tax included
245. save some money
246. cut back in salary
247. paychecks
248. high rollers
249. up front money
250. loan
251. wise investment

page 31

252. send on an errand
253. for sale by owner
254. cash and carry
255. undertake the task
256. day in and day out
257. drop someone a few lines
258. a bad check
259. speculate
260. ATM withdrawals

page 32

261. bar graph
262. number sense
263. inch worm
264. pension rollover
265. sweetheart deal
266. put two and two together
267. parabola
268. business manual